BETH ORTON CENTRAL RESERVATION

Exclusive Distributors:

International Music Publications Limited
Griffin House, 161 Hammersmith Road, London W6 8BS, England
International Music Publications GmbH, Germany
Marstallstraße 8, D-80539 Munchen, Germany

Nuova Carisch S.p.a.
Via Campania, 12 20098 S. Giuliano Milanese (MI)
Zona Industriale Sesto Ulteriano, Italy
20, rue de la Ville-l'Eveque-75008 Paris, France
www.carisch.com

Danmusik
Vognmagergade 7, DK-1120 Copenhagen K, Denmark

Warner/Chappell Music Australia Pty Ltd.
3 Talavera Road, North Ryde, New South Wales 2113, Australia

Folio © 1999 International Music Publications Ltd
Griffin House, 161 Hammersmith Road, London W6 8BS, England

Music Transcribed by Barnes Music Engraving Ltd., East Sussex TN22 4HA
Printed by The Panda Group · Haverhill · Suffolk CB9 8PR · UK · Binding by Haverhill Print Finishers

Write to Beth Orton
c/o Rough Trade Management
66 Golborne Road
London W10 5PS

http://www.bugjuice.com/bethorton/
http://www.heavenly.co.uk/

Photo pages Sam Harris

She's been variously described as a 'bummed out angel in the badlands of love' (Details), 'the clear eyed oracle of London's breakbeat scene' (Spin), and 'Queen of the heartbreak vocal' (Mercury Music Prize judges). There must be something special about Beth Orton that makes people attempt poetry. Ever since her debut solo album *'Trailer Park'* was released to critical acclaim in October '96, people have been enchanted by the collection of lovingly crafted, beguiling songs and entranced by the tall Norfolk broad with the acoustic guitar. With 2 Brit Awards and 2 Mercury Music Prize nominations and a couple of gold albums under her belt, it seems everyone is entranced by the intriguing English girl with the spine-tingling voice and pocketful of heartache.

At six foot tall and disarmingly sharp, Beth Orton is not exactly what you'd expect. With an ability to reduce grown men to tears with her songs, Beth is more likely to steal your last fag than cry on your shoulder. As she says "I don't think my songs are as miserable as people make out. There's a lot of hope in there as well. It depends if you're a half-empty or half-full person". Born in Norfolk in 1970, Beth moved to London with her mother at the age of 14 where they plotted up in Dalston. Her older brothers being punk rockers, the most rebellious thing the teenage Beth could do was get into folk. She spent her late teens immersed in everything, from Nick Drake to The Slits and The Stone Roses to Rickie Lee Jones. After a chance meeting with dance producer William Orbit she was cajoled into embarking on her first musical project, and they wrote *'Water From A Vine Leaf'* together. Having worked with Mr Orbit for two years she co-wrote the first two Red Snapper singles and teamed up with the (little known at the time) Chemical Brothers on *'Alive: Alone'*, the haunting final track on the Brothers' ace debut album.

With a record deal of her own Beth set about: bringing musicians together, finding Ted Barnes, and Ali Friend (from Red Snapper); blending her guitars with samples and beats on an album of starkly personal songs of breathtaking beauty. Working with producers Victor Van Vugt (Tindersticks, Nick Cave) and Andrew Weatherall (producer of the classic 'Screamadelica') she created her own brand of rhythm-infused folk. *'Trailer Park'* struck a chord with everyone from seasoned folkies, country aficionados, teenage clubbers and the broken hearted. She then led her new band on a year long road trek supporting various bands before selling out her own headline tours.

Pausing only to supply vocals to The Chemical Brothers' globe conquering *'Dig Your Own Hole'* album before throwing herself straight into another record of her own, her second long player, *'Central Reservation'* was released in March 1999 and found Beth duly catapulted into the stratosphere. Sonically leaps and bounds from her intriguing debut *'Central Reservation'* saw Beth hook up again with Victor Van Vugt as well as David Roback (from Mazzy Star), Ben Watt (from Everything But The Girl), Ben Harper, Terry Callier and Dr John. The album is a simultaneously wide-screen and profoundly personal collection of folk-trip-dub-rock songs soundtracking life as she knows it, full of harsh sorrows and magical joy. A profoundly gifted musician, Beth Orton manages to blend her eclectic influences into a unique and solitary style that is immediately recognisable and defiantly individual. Taking that into account how hundreds of thousands of music lovers in the UK and America have embraced her records, it's really only a matter of time before the rest of the world bows to reason and Beth Orton becomes the household name she truly deserves to be.

Stolen Car

Words by Beth Orton
Music by Beth Orton, Ted Barnes,
Sean Read and William Blanchard

Sweetest Decline

Words and Music by
Beth Orton

Couldn't Cause Me Harm

Words by Beth Orton
Music by Beth Orton, Ted Barnes,
Sean Read and William Blanchard

1. Ooh yeah, you know you could - n't cause me a - ny harm.
2. And if I told you, would you ne - ver know to guess?

So Much More

Words and Music by
Beth Orton

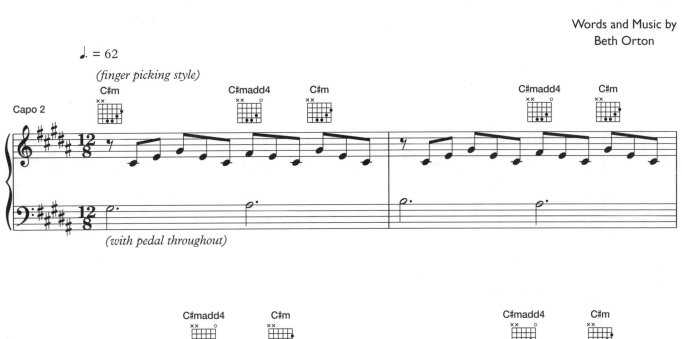

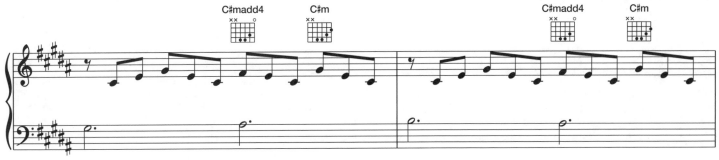

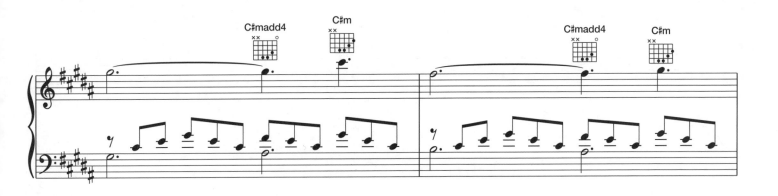

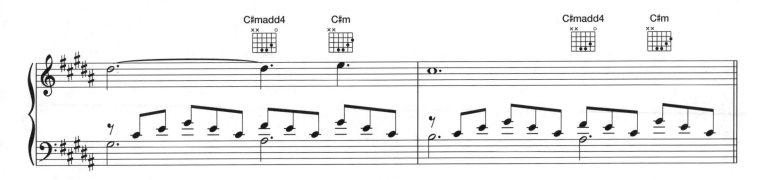

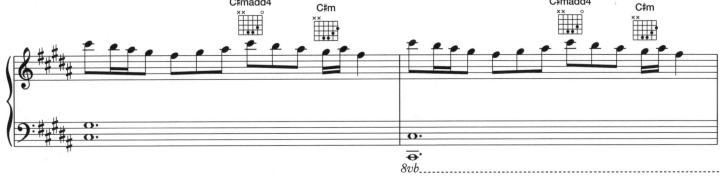

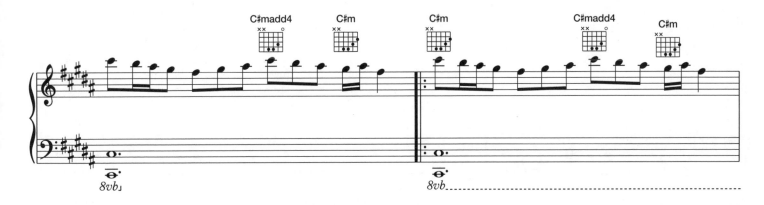

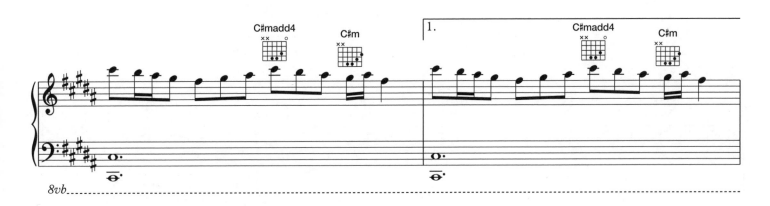

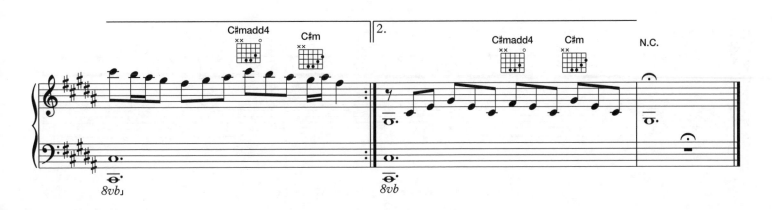

Pass In Time

Words and Music by
Beth Orton

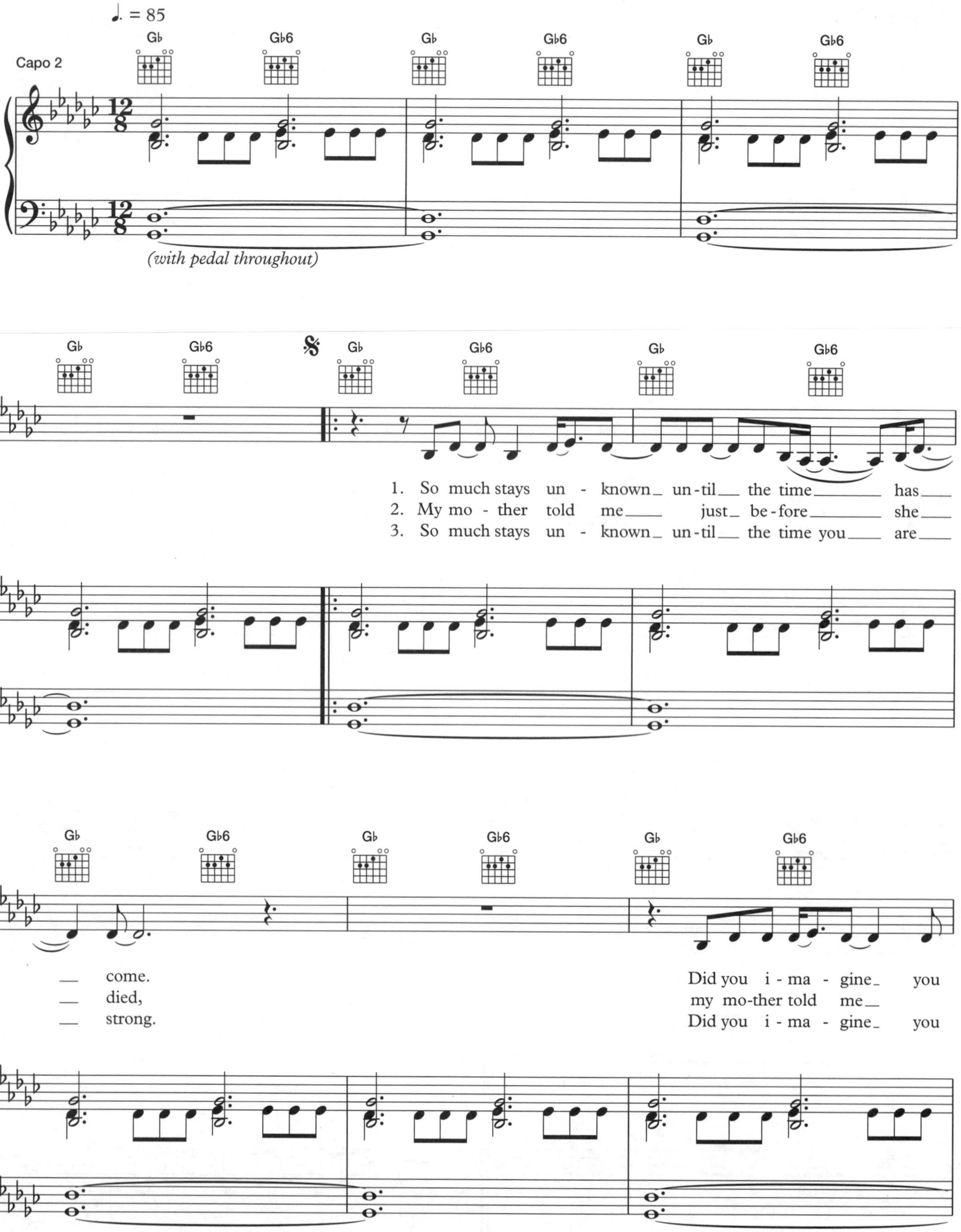

♩. = 85
Capo 2
G♭ G♭6 G♭ G♭6 G♭ G♭6
(with pedal throughout)
G♭ G♭6 G♭ G♭6 G♭ G♭6
1. So much stays un - known_ un-til_ the time_ has_
2. My mo - ther told me_ just_ be-fore_ she_
3. So much stays un - known_ un-til_ the time you_ are_
G♭ G♭6 G♭ G♭6 G♭ G♭6
_ come.
_ died,
_ strong.
Did you i - ma - gine_ you
my mo-ther told me_
Did you i - ma - gine_ you

to Coda ⊕

you're here just___ a_____ while._____

1.

2.

You're here just__ a_____ while._____

Central Reservation
(Original Version)

Words and Music by
Beth Orton

Ooh____ yeah, yeah,__ yeah, yeah, yeah, yeah,_____ yeah,_ yeah.__

Ba-da-ba,__ ba-da-ba,__ ba-da-ba-ba-ba-da-ba-ba-ba - da-ba - ba-ba-da -

- da. Ba-da-n - da-ba-do.

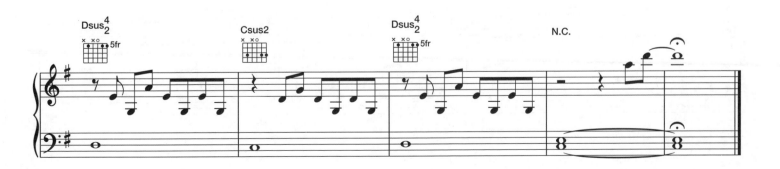

Stars All Seem To Weep

Words and Music by
Beth Orton

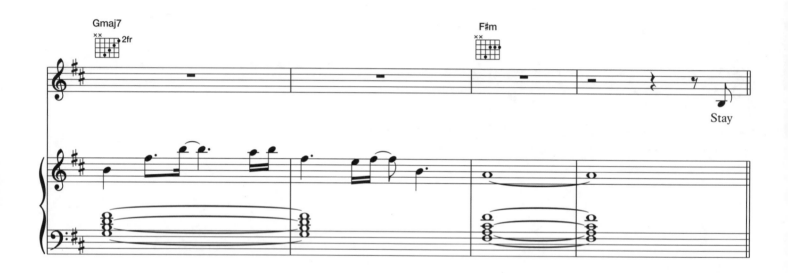

(with pedal throughout)

Look at me do - ing all these things with - out____ you, we al - ways laughed at and you____

Love Like Laughter

Words by Beth Orton
Music by Beth Orton and Ted Barnes

Lyrics:

1. Some of the worst wrongs get right-ed on three chords, like a pro-mise or a kiss good-bye. When the sneer on your lips is the liv-

2. Love is like laugh-ter, see it hap-pened by chance, like a pro-mise be a kiss good-bye. When the smile on your lips is the liv-

Blood Red River

Words and Music by
Beth Orton

Devil Song

Words and Music by
Beth Orton

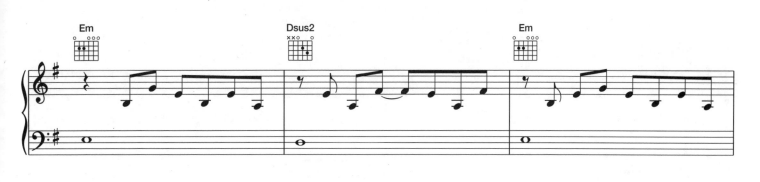

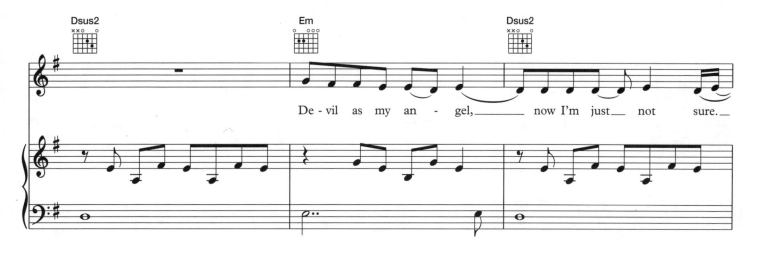

De - vil as my an - gel,_____ now I'm just___ not sure.___

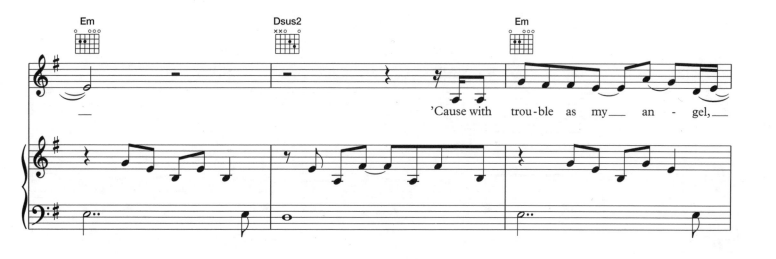

___ gel,__ 'Cause with trou - ble as my__ an - gel,___

_____ there's al - ways more._____ Re -

Feel To Believe

Words and Music by
Beth Orton

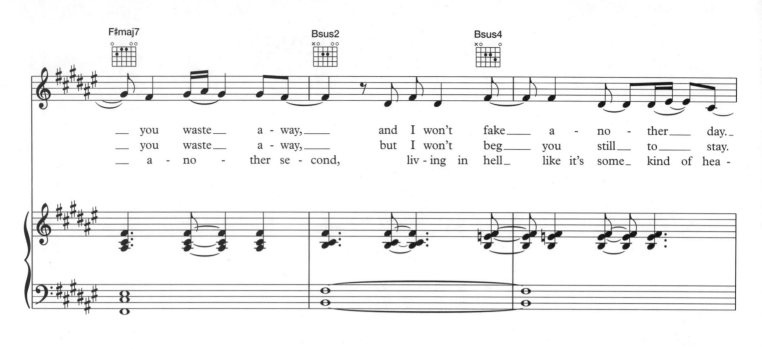

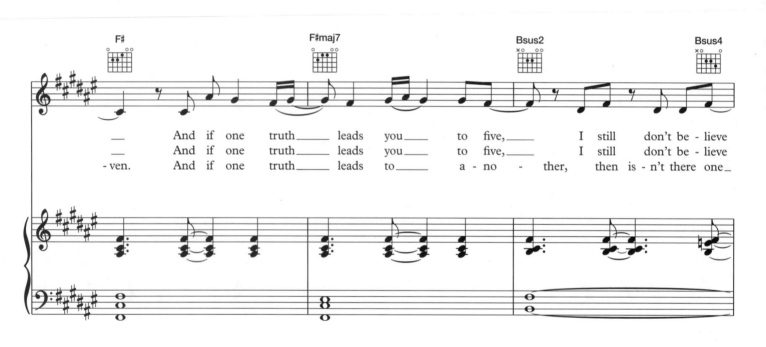

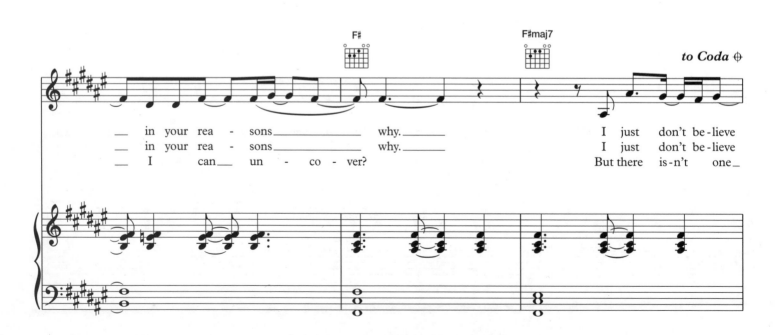

Central Reservation

(The Then Again Version)

Words and Music by
Beth Orton

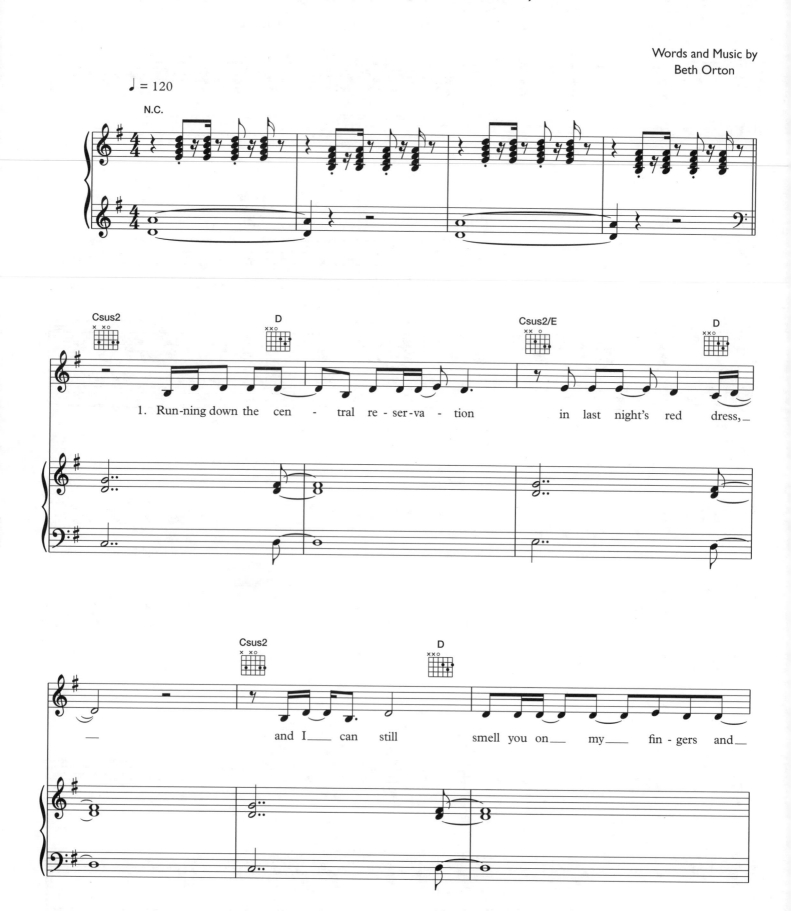